Exploring Me

A Guided Journal for Self-Discovery
and Creative Expression

MARA KRAUSZ

Illustrated by MADALINA TANTAREANU

Illustrations by Madalina Tantareanu
Book design by Sarah Darby

ISBN 978-0-578-81913-6

Marluna Press
P.O. Box 1004
Sierra Madre, CA 91025
www.MarlunaPress.com

Discover your own
unique path

Contents

Suggestions for coloring

Colored pencils are recommended. Markers are not advised since they may show through the paper. Colored pencils are also blendable and easy to use. You may want to put a couple blank sheets of paper below the page you're coloring to reduce any indentation marks.

Introduction

Come explore the magic that is you. Take a little journey of self-reflection, contemplation, and of course, coloring. I invite you to discover new things, release some of the old, and even shift your perspective, all the while embracing what makes you distinctly special. This unique combination of guided journal and coloring book will help you to express your creativity as you delve into your inner world and get to know yourself better.

As a guided journal, it invites you to explore topics of introspection, well-being, and empowerment. Each selection, based on a letter of the alphabet, presents a set of questions. Don't overanalyze your answers—there isn't a right or best response. Simply answer authentically based on how you feel in the moment. If you want to add something else later, feel free. There are no rules for how to use this journal. Just follow your intuition. Each of us is on a unique journey. Discover your own truths, and embrace your inner guidance.

Indulge in a little self-care as you relax and embrace the calming effects of coloring. Coloring can help reduce stress, spark creativity, and even be a form of meditation. Plus, it's a fun, easy way to reconnect with the kid in you. As you consider the questions, coloring can help you to relax and tune into your intuition. Or perhaps you simply want to color and enjoy this time to yourself. The choice is yours. This is your journal to use however you like. Now break out the colored pencils and enjoy!

Abundance

When you think about the word abundance, what thoughts and feelings arise?

What are your beliefs about creating and having abundance? Who or what has influenced these beliefs?

What are some non-monetary forms of abundance that are meaningful to you?

What are you grateful to have an abundance of in your life?
What would you like to create more of (including non-material wants or needs)? What steps are you taking toward this?

Believe

If someone asked if you believe in yourself, how would you respond?

What is something you used to believe that you'd like to renew your confidence in? Why did you stop believing? What's a first step you can take toward regaining this trust?

When you were a child, did someone say something untrue or disheartening that you believed, and it had a ripple effect?
What would you now tell your younger self?

If you could believe that your life isn't limited by circumstances or past decisions, how would your actions change?

Compassion

What does compassion mean to you? Do you show the same compassion for yourself as for others? Explain.

In what areas and circumstances do you not exhibit enough compassion (both toward yourself and others)? Why do you withhold this compassion?

What role has compassion played in your relationships?

What is an unexpected moment of compassion that impacted you?
Describe the effect it had.

Dreams⭐

What are your dreams? What role do they currently play in your life?

In what ways have the words, judgments, or beliefs of others impacted you in following your dreams? If they've had an adverse effect, how can you shift your mindset and actions to reduce their influence?

What is your inner dialog regarding your dreams? In what ways can you shift this to be more encouraging, constructive, or empowering?

List the reasons that your dreams are possible, achievable, and happening.

Empower

Being empowered means_____. What examples of empowerment (either observed or through your own experiences) have had an impact on you? What did you learn?

What concerns or fears sometimes stop you from stepping into your power? Examine how these may not be as limiting or formidable as you perceive them to be.

What can you do to feel more empowered when you need a small boost and when you need a bigger one?

What's the most empowered you've ever felt? What can you take from that experience to help you feel empowered more consistently?

Forgiveness

What does it feel like to forgive someone? How does it feel when someone forgives you? How does it feel when you forgive yourself?

What's something you would like to forgive someone for but are finding it difficult? What's another perspective to view it from? Describe how your life would be different if you released this weight.

What is something you'd like to forgive yourself for but haven't yet?
Why do you find this self-forgiveness to be difficult?

How did you learn and grow from an uncomfortable situation that
you brought forgiveness into? What positives did you emerge with?

Gratitude

Make a list of what you are grateful for in your life and in the world. Include aspects of yourself that you're grateful for.

What experiences and people are you grateful for? How did they impact you?

Throughout your day, express gratitude. At the end of the day, write down how it affected your emotional state or attitude.

What have you always wanted to thank someone for but haven't? What words of gratitude do you have for them?

What would you like to heal? Do you notice any patterns or themes? What is a first step you can take toward healing?

What is your usual approach to healing? How well do you feel this has worked in the past? What might you do differently in the future?

List any beliefs or "stories" you tell yourself that may be hindering your healing process. Can you identify their origin? What is a step you can take toward releasing them?

What activities have a healing effect on you? How can you integrate them more fully into your lifestyle?

Intuition

When do you listen to or value other people's intuition more than your own? Why do you give their intuition precedence in these circumstances?

Do you give more importance to reasoning or intuition? Why?

How often do you follow your intuition? Why do you sometimes not trust or listen to your intuition? How can you further develop this trust?

What has your intuition taught you?

Joy

How important is embracing joy to you? What activities and experiences nourish this joy?

What are some little things you can do to shift yourself into a place of joy when you need a quick pick-me-up?

How can you share more joy with those around you?

When do you feel the most joyful and happy? What can you do to embrace this feeling more often?

Kindness

What acts of kindness (large or small) can you engage in more often?

How can you be kind to yourself when you're hurting?

In what areas of your life would you like more kindness to be present? Include both giving and receiving.

What experiences, people, or animals have taught you the most about kindness?

Light

What does "shine your light" mean to you?

When do you most often hesitate in shining your light? Why?

How can you more fully embrace shining your light? What are some actions you can take and disempowering thoughts you can shift?

When does your light shine brightest?

Meaning

Where have you searched for meaning and not been able to find it?
Where have you found meaning?

What's an unexpected place or moment where you've found meaning?

What meaningful interactions and experiences have you had: with someone you just met; with someone or something outside of your comfort zone; while traveling?

How have your most meaningful experiences shaped you?

Nurture

Do you take time to nurture yourself? If not, why don't you?
Do you nurture others before yourself?

What actions can you take to nurture yourself both on a daily basis
and when more in-depth nurturing is needed?

What little things can you do to make your living space more nurturing?

What are your favorite activities, experiences, and creative pursuits to nurture your mind, body, and soul?

Observe

Observe your physical body's needs. What needs do you most often ignore and why? How can you treat your body with more care?

Observe when you judge yourself and others. List what you're most judgmental about. Why do these trigger you?

Observe your thoughts. When and how often are they fear-based or disempowering? When and how often are they confident or hopeful?

Observe when you feel the most calm and centered. What do you notice about these moments and how they were created so you can replicate them more often?

Positivity

When and how has keeping a positive mindset benefited you?
What have you learned from these experiences?

In what areas of your life can you have a more positive attitude?
Give examples of what this positive attitude might look like.

What have you learned about positivity from those who embrace it?

For a day, focus on positive thoughts and use positive words.
At the end of the day, reflect on how you felt and what you noticed.

Questions

If you could choose one question to be given the answer to, what would it be? Why did you choose that question?

What is a question you've always wanted to ask someone close to you but felt unable to do so or were too nervous about the potential answer?

What question would you like to ask your inner child? What would you ask your inner wisdom?

Is there a significant moment when you questioned your perspective or beliefs? What did you learn, and how did it impact you?

Reflect

Look at your reflection in the mirror. What thoughts and feelings arise?

The moon reflects light from the sun. What do you reflect?

In what ways do you see your thoughts and emotions reflected in your external experiences?

What areas of your life (or what aspects of yourself) do you avoid delving into? Why are you avoiding this self-reflection? What benefits could come from it?

Self-Talk

What are the most common things you tell yourself on a daily basis? What does observing this self-talk show you, and what can you learn?

What self-judgments and self-criticisms do you commonly make? Where do they stem from? How can you reshape them into something more constructive?

When you feel doubt or fear arising, what do you tell yourself to shift into a more empowered mindset?

What positive and empowering messages do you have for your adult self? What loving words do you have for your inner child?

Transform

If you could transform like a caterpillar into a butterfly, what would you transform from and into?

What habit, pattern, or fear would you most like to transform?
What is something positive and empowered it can become?

What event or experience resulted in your most significant transformation?

What transformation would you like to create in your life this year?

Unconditional Love

What does unconditional love mean to you?

Do you ever withhold unconditional love from yourself? Explain why you sometimes do this, and give an example.

Is there someone you're seeking unconditional love from that doesn't know how to give it? In what ways could you shift your perspective to allow for forgiveness or acceptance of that which you cannot change?

What have you learned from others (including animals) about unconditional love? Describe some of these impactful experiences.

Do you feel that other people's needs have more value than your own? If so, why? What rationalizations do you make when you don't prioritize yourself or set healthy boundaries?

What are some early memories of not believing in or questioning your value? What was their impact? How can you now shift your perspective?

What changes can you make to your actions and way of thinking that affirm and support your value and self-worth?

What are some self-care practices you can do to honor and value YOU?

What words would you use to describe yourself? How would you also describe your strengths, as well as what makes you unique?

How much influence do you give to the words spoken by others? When do you give them precedence over your own words or voice and why?

Use your own unique words (and not the words of others) to describe your philosophy on life.

What are some of the most meaningful words someone has ever said to you? Reflect on how you felt and ways that you can use your words to help others.

X-ray

Use your x-ray vision to delve into your beliefs. What beliefs might you be questioning? List your reasons for reevaluating them. What now feels more resonant?

Take an x-ray of your insecurities. When do you most often seek approval, acceptance, or validation from others? Why are these scenarios a trigger for you?

Use your x-ray vision to examine when there's a disconnect between your words and your actions. When does this happen most often? Is there a common theme or rationalization you make?

Use your x-ray vision to delve into self-love. List at least five things that you love about yourself.

Younger

The loving wisdom I would share with my early childhood self is:

The gentle guidance I would give my high school self is:

The compassionate counsel I'd share with my 20s/30s self is:

The words of wisdom I'd impart to my 40s and above self is:

Zest

The zest of a lemon or orange enhances the vibrancy of many recipes. What zest adds vibrancy to your life?

How would you describe your current zest for life? What tends to dampen your zest, and what tends to increase it? How can you embrace your zest more fully?

Give some examples of people who personify zest for life.

What have you observed that you can incorporate into your own life?

What activities or experiences encapsulate the feeling of zest for you?

ABOUT THE AUTHOR

Mara Krausz is a Los Angeles-based writer of books and television, specializing in personal development and romantic comedy. Her work has appeared in the Boston Globe. Prior to writing, she took a delicious detour through the world of chocolate as a co-founder of an artisanal chocolate company.

CPSIA information can be obtained
at www.ICGtesting.com
Printed in the USA
JSHW012235010221
11445JS00010B/88